DEAR *mom*

★ ★ ★ ★ ★ ★ ★

KNOCK
KNOCK®
VENICE, CALIFORNIA

Original text by Gerard Janssen
(and some of your own!)

Artwork by Petra Baan
(and some of your own!)

Originally published in Dutch by Uitgeverij Snor
© 2010 by Uitgeverij Snor
All rights reserved
Published in English by
Who's There Inc. d/b/a Knock Knock
Venice, CA 90291
knockknockstuff.com

Translation © 2014 Who's There Inc.
All rights reserved
Knock Knock is a trademark of Who's There Inc.
Made in China

The rights to this book have been negotiated by
the literary agency Sea of Stories
www.seaofstories.com

*Thanks to you I am (almost)
always at school on time,
so I can learn a lot and will soon be
able to write beautiful legalese too.*

ISBN: 978-160106601-5
UPC: 825703-31050-4

10 9 8 7 6 5 4 3 2 1

FOR MOM

From your genius son/daughter:

(Write your name here.)

DEAR MOM,

I am so happy you found (or replaced!) all these things I've lost before:

Circle items you've lost.

Oh, and also:

(Draw or paste items.)

dear mom,

You always look so sweet/caring/tired/concerned/ . . .

 Put an X in each ☐ that has a pic like your mom.

My mom looks completely different than that! She looks like this:

(Draw your mom here.)

my mother's name is:

But a better name for her would be:

☐ Superstar

☐ Kisses Fairy

☐ Heart Catapult

☐ Mary ⟶

☐ Penelope

 smack

☐ Petunia

☐ Fantasia

☐ Hug Muffin

☐ Sweet Candy

☐ Tallest Mountain in the World

☐ Galloping Amazon

Oh, and also:

- -

- -

dear mom, *You're amazingly good at:*

☐ Listening	☐ Baking cakes
☐ Hugging	☐ Brushing hair
☐ Cooking	☐ Getting gum out of stuff
☐ Organizing	☐ Tucking me in at night
☐ Doing math	☐ Horsing around
☐ Drawing graphs	☐ Helping with homework
☐ Writing notes	☐ Playing on your iPhone
☐ Boxing	☐ Reading to me

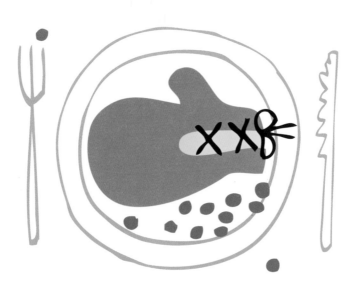

 Place a checkmark next to the things your mom is good at.

And other things, like:

This is what I want to be when I grow up:

- Video game tester
- Candy taster
- Pastry chef
- Chocolate maker
- Astronaut
- Pilot
- Cloud professor
- Tech whiz
- Pig farmer
- Realtor
- Cleaner
- Dermatologist
- Hairdresser
- Money-factory boss
- Lawyer

dear mom,

When you're mad, you always say:

GEE WHIZ

SHOOT

DARN IT

You don't allow me to say this . . .

Do I have to do everything myself?

BLAST IT

WOWOWO

That does it!

SANTIAGO

RATS

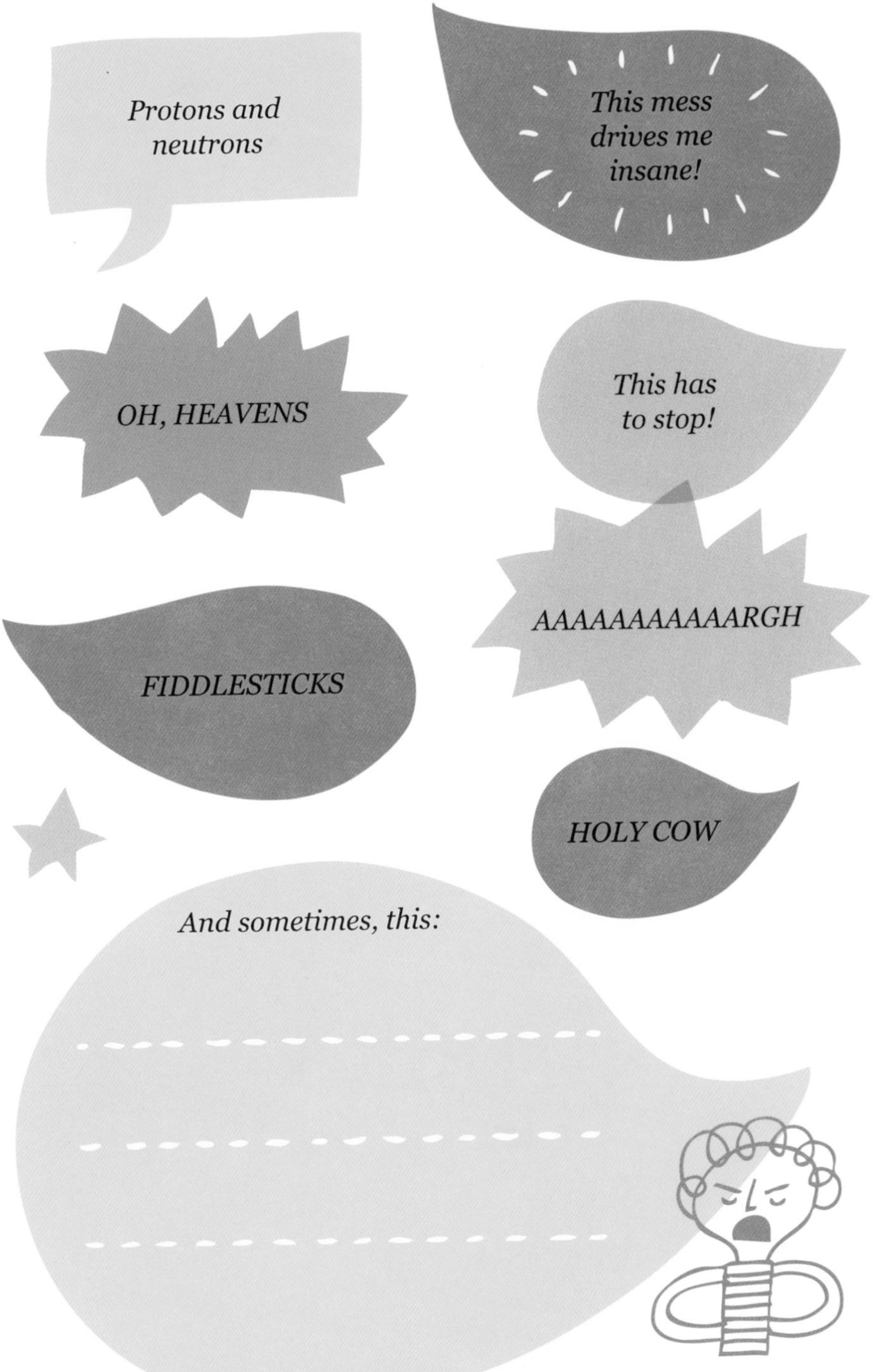
Protons and neutrons
This mess drives me insane!
OH, HEAVENS
This has to stop!
AAAAAAAAAAARGH
FIDDLESTICKS
HOLY COW
And sometimes, this:

dear mom,

When you're happy, you always say:

And we're still a long, long way from home.

Isn't this fun!?

I am having such a good time!

HOORAY! HOORAY!

HOORAY!

SWELL

I bought a lottery ticket.

Shall we go for a nice walk?

We need a new fridge.

It's fabulous!

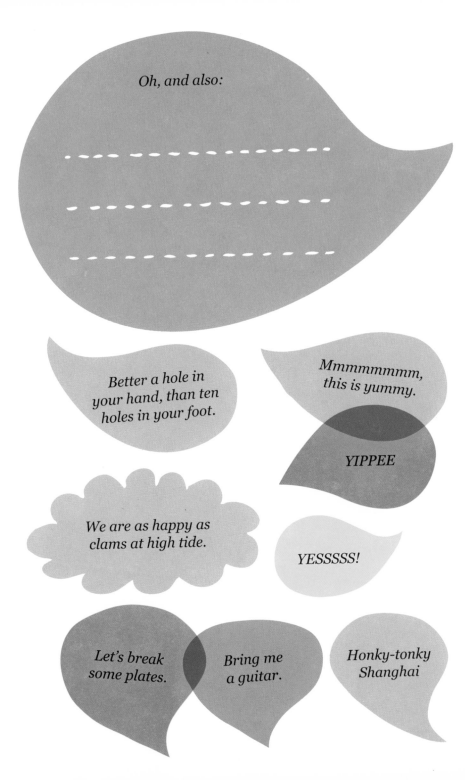

dear mom,

Without you, I'd feel like a:

PB&J without the jelly

Hippopotamus with antlers

Parrot with no feathers

Donut without a hole

Crane that can't lift stuff

Shoe without laces

Forest without trees

Circle how you feel when your mom's away.

Oh, and also:

- -

- -

- -

- -

(Write down how you'd feel if your mom wasn't around. Or just make a drawing!)

dear mom,

This is what I think you looked like when you were my age:

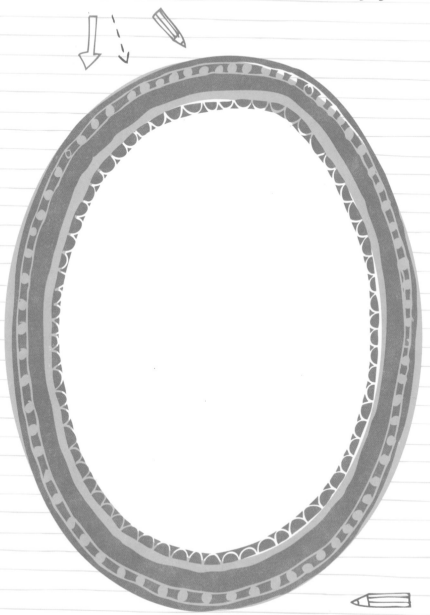

 Make a drawing of what you think your mom looked like when she was young.

This is what I think I'll look like when I'm your age:

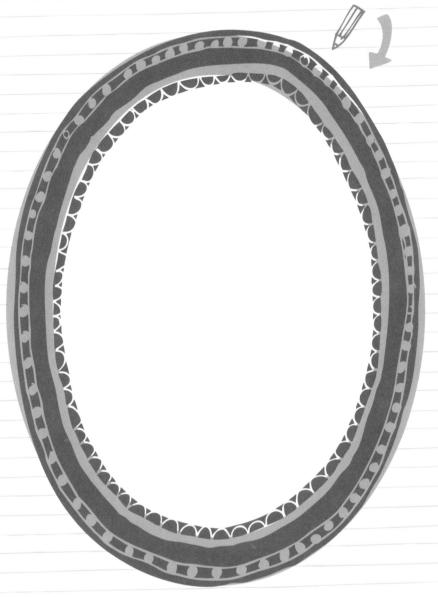

 Make a drawing of what you think you'll look like when you're older.

dear mom,

When you're at work, this is what I think you do:

- ☐ Staple stuff
- ☐ Write stories
- ☐ Use big words when you talk
- ☐ Walk up and down the stairs
- ☐ Stare at your computer
- ☐ Drink coffee
- ☐ Talk and talk and talk
- ☐ Eat candy
- ☐ Blow bubbles
- ☐ Wheel around on your rolling chair
- ☐ Pin things with tacks
- ☐ Talk on the phone

 Put a checkmark next to the things you think your mom does at work.

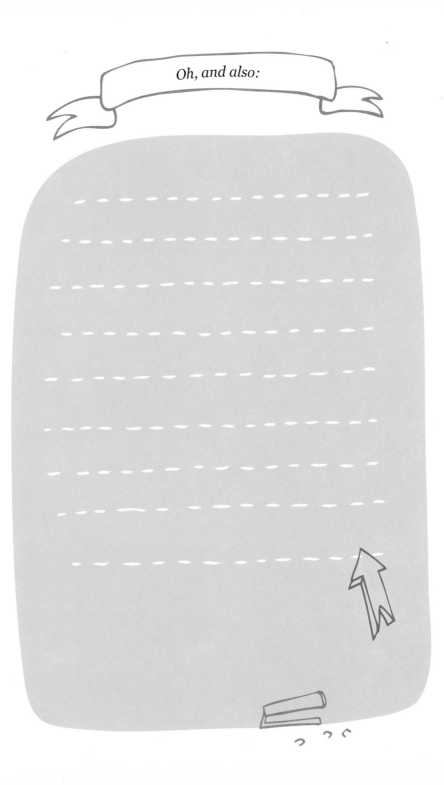

Oh, and also:

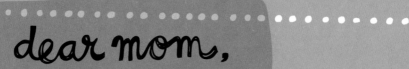

dear mom,

The most fun thing that
happened to us in the last year is:

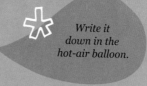

**Write it
down in the
hot-air balloon.**

DEAR MOM,

You talk a lot about:

 Color in the item(s) your mom talks about most.

Oh, and also:

(Write or draw what your mom talks about most.)

dear mom, Bet you didn't know that I . . .

. . . would love to
spend the whole day:

. . . dream about:

. . . am very good at:

. . . want to whisper
this secret to you:

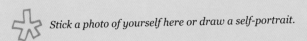 *Stick a photo of yourself here or draw a self-portrait.*

burp

dear mom,

I always laugh out loud when you . . .

- ☐ dance like crazy
- ☐ pretend to vacuum me
- ☐ do yoga
- ☐ get mad
- ☐ walk in high heels
- ☐ say inappropriate words
- ☐ hang upside-down in a tree
- ☐ have the giggles
- ☐ pick something up with your toes
- ☐ pass gas/burp
- ☐ imitate the neighbor
- ☐ tickle me

tickle tickle

Oh, and also:

(Write down what makes you laugh.)

Oh yeah, before I forget, this is what I would like for my birthday:

example

✳ *Draw, write, or paste pics of the presents you'd like to get.*

dear mom, I don't really like these clothes at all:

✳ *Color in the clothes you don't like.*

too short!

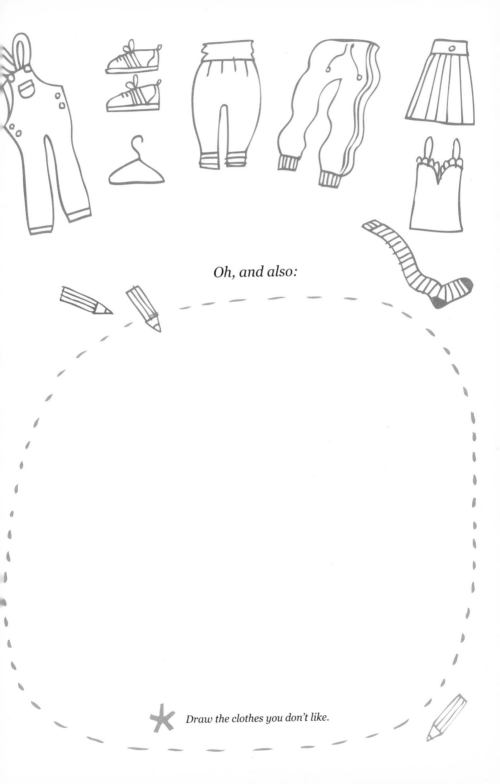

Oh, and also:

Draw the clothes you don't like.

dear mom,

When I grow up to be rich, I will buy you all these things:

- ☐ Camel
- ☐ Palace
- ☐ Island
- ☐ A fancy birdcage
- ☐ Unicorn
- ☐ Chocolate factory
- ☐ The Sun
- ☐ A million lottery tickets
- ☐ Ice-cream machine
- ☐ Amusement park
- ☐ Pink diamond
- ☐ Vacuum cleaner robot
- ☐ Aardvark
- ☐ Golden laptop
- ☐ Facelift
- ☐ Baby polar bear

Oh, and also:

dear mom, I think this would look good on you:

(Color in the items you'd like your mom to wear.)

Oh, and also:

DEAR MOM,

Here's a paper badge for you!

Cut out your favorite badges and give them to your mom!

I got this from my **CHILD**

I am always right

TURBO MAMA

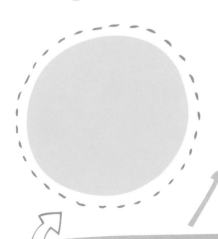

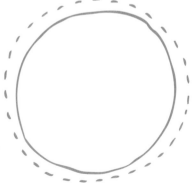

Decorate a badge for your mom.

Cutout page

dear mom,

You're a real octopus!

 Draw things your mom often holds in her hands. For example, a laptop, a scrub brush, a book, a cellphone, a tennis racket, etc.

my mom loves...

* Color in all the items your mom loves.

me

Oh, and also:

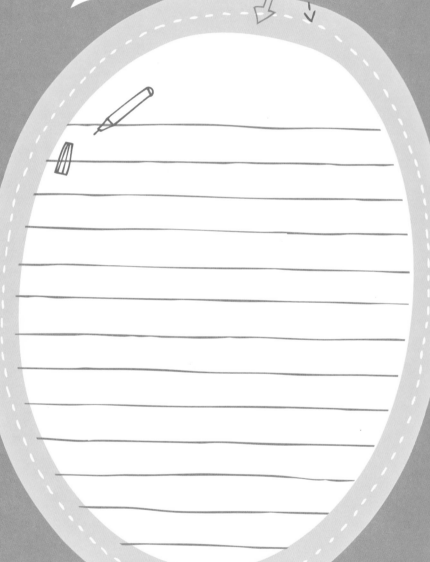

Here's how I'm a lot like you:

big kiss!